Why Dying

Of

Addiction

By

Wale Oyeniyi

Table of Contents

Introduction

Addiction is a human condition that has been around for ages. The condition is arguably as old as humanity itself.

The Advanced English Dictionary defines addiction as "being abnormally tolerant to and dependent on something that is psychologically or physically habit-forming (especially alcohol or narcotic drugs)".

It can be said that since men learned how to enjoy things, addiction has slowly but surely emerged. If something can be enjoyed, then one can develop an addiction to it.

Addiction has caused men sorrow and devastation since the days of Sodom and Gomorrah in the Old Testament.

In (Genesis 19), the Bible records the destruction of the people of Sodom and Gomorrah who, according to the Scriptures were chronic sinners—folks addicted to all forms of sinful act.

The story was told of how they insisted on knowing the men (angels) that came to visit Lot. Verse 9 says, "And they said, Stand back. And they said again, this one fellow came in to sojourn, and he will need to be a judge: now will we deal worse with thee, than with them. And they pressed sore upon the man, even Lot, and came near to break the door.

They were relentless in the pursuit of the fulfillment of their carnal passions.

Even before God destroyed Sodom and Gomorrah, he had destroyed some people earlier for the same reasons. The first seven verses of Genesis 6 speak of the wickedness of men that stemmed from man's overindulgence in his carnal passions.

(Genesis 6:5) says,

"And God saw that the wickedness of man was great in the earth, and that every imagination of the thoughts of his heart was only evil continually."

A little further in verses 11 and 12 it says,

"The earth also was corrupt before God, and the earth was filled with violence. And God looked upon the earth, and, behold, it was corrupt; for all flesh had corrupted his way upon the earth".

This led to His verdict in verse 13,

"And God said unto Noah, The end of all flesh is come before me; for the earth is filled with violence through them; and, behold, I will destroy them with the earth."

The world today is arguably as worse as the Sodom and Gomorrah of those days. Almost every single one of us is addicted to something these days.

Some are addicted to corrupt and debased practices of all sorts, while there are those whose addiction, though spiritually harmless are no less mentally harmful.

So many people who look good on the outside are slaves to different forms of carnal passions in their closets. Addiction has led many a man and woman down several ignoble lanes. This menace has taken many men and women from high places to disgrace and disrepute. It has ruined careers and buried talents. It has truncated marriages and destinies alike. And it still does all of these every day. Every day, every hour, every minute, addiction claims another victim.

The battle to conquer addiction is one that most people fail in because they are usually in it alone. A lot of people endeavor to fight addiction without any significant help and the result of this is that they continue to relapse and fall even deeper into the abysmal ditch.

In my lifetime, I've seen people claimed by all sorts of addiction and I'm deeply overwhelmed. I then decided to do something about it. I could no longer watch men and women continue to go down this destructive lane, so I decided to write this book to help anyone who will diligently read and follow the insights shared in the book.

Addiction easily leads to sin as much as it's a sin in itself. It is a form of overindulgence which means at a point, it consumes one's heart and soul. When a person's heart is preoccupied with something else apart from God, such a thing becomes their god.

I once read that the destruction of the soul always originates from the desires of the heart, and I couldn't agree more. The spirit of addiction is against the Spirit of God.

The Bible says in (John 8:34),

"Jesus answered them, Verily, verily, I say unto you, Whosoever committeth sin is the servant of sin".

Whoever is addicted becomes a slave unto that to which he is addicted. The moment the desire for something takes utmost priority in a person's life, such desires assume the position of god. As believers, nothing except God should take the utmost priority in our life.

The insights shared in this book are based on the latest discoveries in science. They are also founded on the eternal word of God because deliverance and salvation can only be found in the Almighty. No matter how strong the cord of bondage is, it is never too strong for God to break. No matter how deep you have descended into the pits of addiction, the creator who created you without any addiction can redeem you.

Most people think that they can break their addiction by sheer willpower, but they soon find out that sheer willpower is not enough. Willpower has a funny way of letting us down when we need it most. If we must break the chains of addiction, we need a force that is greater than us, a power that is greater than the stranglehold of our addiction on our person—spirit, soul and body.

This sort of power can only be found in the Almighty. The Scriptures put it aptly way in (Romans 6:5-6),

"For if we have been planted together in the likeness of his death, we shall be also in the likeness of his resurrection: Knowing this, that our old man is crucified with him, that the body of sin might be destroyed, that henceforth we should not serve sin."

So as you read through the insights in this book, let it be at the back of your mind that the ultimate solution is in Christ. It is when you apply the insights in Christ that you can claim your eventual victory over the deadly foe called addiction.

The knowledge shared in this book are inspired but it won't do you any good if you don't make conscious efforts to apply them. Like the words of God in the Scriptures, the insights are powerful and are capable of changing your life but if you don't consciously apply the wisdom, there won't be any difference whatsoever. It takes a lot of self-control backed by the grace of God to avoid or escape the detention of addiction.

It is well with you!

Chapter 1: What Is Addiction?

The Center on Addiction defines addiction as a complex disease, often chronic in nature, which affects the functioning of the brain and body.

www.medicalnewstoday.com has a better definition, according to them:

"addiction is a psychological and physical inability to stop consuming a chemical, drug, activity, or substance, even though it is causing psychological and physical harm.

American Psychiatric Association defines addiction as "a complex condition, a brain disease that is manifested by compulsive substance use despite harmful consequence."

To further put things in perspective, let me repeat the definition cited earlier from the Advanced English Dictionary. They define addiction "as being abnormally tolerant to and dependent on something that is psychologically or physically habit-forming (especially alcohol or narcotic drugs)."

One thing stands out from all these definitions and it is that addiction is a chronic and compulsive abnormality. It is a psychological problem with physical manifestations. It is a disease and a condition which affects the brain and the body. It is a situation whereby a person is unable to stop using or doing something, even when such a thing is causing them significant psychological and physical harm.

An addiction is a damaging habit that is rather hard to break despite the victim being aware of its damaging effect in one way or the other. It is a mental disorder, a disruption of the normal functioning of the brain and mind.

Addiction goes beyond the manifesting physical habits, it is a problem deeply rooted in the mind where it continues to fester if not strongly checked and eventually removed. Brain imaging studies show changes in the areas of the brain that relate to judgment, decision making, learning, memory and behaviour control of addicted people.

Interestingly, when most people hear the word 'addiction', they tend to think about inordinate dependence on chemicals and substances such as cocaine, heroin or alcohol. But the term 'addiction' goes beyond just that. An individual who is unable to stop using a specific substance or chemical has substance dependence.

A number of addictions, however, involve an inability to stop engaging in certain activities such as eating, sex or gambling, in what is regarded as behavioural addictions. In essence, one can be addicted to a substance or an activity. It is not only substance or chemical that an individual can be addicted to. People now get addicted to internet gaming, shopping and even social media.

When a person is experiencing addiction, they are unable to control how they consume a substance or participate in an activity, and they become dependent on such a substance or activity to cope with daily life. They find it hard to cope with their daily life if they don't get the sufficient dose of their stimulant. The normal state becomes intolerable to them, and their state after getting the right dose of their specific fix assumes the 'new normal' state. The 'high' state becomes the normal state for the addicted person. Once they are out of this state, they feel like a fish out of water. They become restless and experience some sort of excruciating misery in what is known as a withdrawal symptom, which is any physical or psychological disturbance (as sweating or depression) experienced by an addict when deprived of the thing to which they are addicted.

The majority of individuals begin to use a drug or first got involved in an activity voluntarily. People use substances like alcohol or drugs, or an activity such as gaming or use of social media to escape, relax or as a reward. These stuffs over time are however capable of making you think that you require them to enjoy life as it were, or that you are incapable of coping without them which can progressively degenerate into dependence and eventually addiction.

As such, addiction is capable of taking over initially occasional activities and reducing self-control. Addiction does not happen overnight. It is a disease that grows and intensifies over time. It develops gradually and progressively until it becomes full-blown and requiring serious medical attention.

An addiction must tick at least three (3) of the following conditions. This is based on the criteria of the American Psychiatric Association (The Diagnostic and Statistical Manual of Mental Disorders-IV) and World Health Organization (International Classification of Diseases-10).

Tolerance

This has to do with the usage of the activity or substance over time.

Withdrawal

This concerns the emotional or physical withdrawal that addicts experience when they stop using the activity or substance. The experience could include shakes, nausea, sweats, irritability, anxiety, or vomiting. Emotional withdrawal is just as important as physical withdrawal.

Limited Control

This manifests in the use of substance or activity more than the addict like. It concerns using substance to get to the point of stupor and regretting the amount used in previous times, e. g. the previous day.

Negative Consequences

This involves continued use of substance or activity despite negative consequences to self-esteem, mood, family, job or health.

Abandoned Or Deferred Activities

This manifests in the putting off or reduction of social, household, work, or recreational activities due to addict's abnormal use of activity or substance.

Significant time or energy spent. Addicts spend a noteworthy amount of time procuring, using, hiding, planning, or convalescing from their use. They expend a lot of time thinking about using. They also spend time trying to conceal or minimize their use. They diligently contrive schemes to avoid getting caught in their use.

Desire To Cut Down

Addict sometimes think about cutting down or controlling their use. They make a lot of unsuccessful attempts to cut down or control their use.

What Causes Addiction?

Addiction is an effect, an outcome. On the other hand, it can also be a cause of many other issues. However, addiction is primarily an outcome, which means that there are causes of addiction. It becomes easier to understand addiction when we think through how we are wired biologically to seek pleasure.

There are several theories on addiction causes. Some argue that it is determined genetically, while others contend at the other end that it is a result of purely environmental elements, such as a troubled childhood. The disease model which is dominant considers addiction as a biological "disease" whereby the addictive substance or activity essentially takes over the brain, resulting in lasting biochemical changes and thereby making addiction certain.

However, there are many other contending theories. For instance, some suggest that addiction is more reliant on conditioned behaviours and dysfunctional thoughts; that addiction is a spiritual or moral issue, or that addiction stems from a deficiency of social connection.

A large percentage of psychologists today agree that addiction stems from intricate interaction of several elements, including psychological, biological, social and even spiritual factors (for some). This is known as the Bio-Psycho-Social-Spiritual (BPSS) Model1.

Biological Causes

Addiction is a problem of brain functioning and this is why willpower is not enough to combat it. We become hooked to the chemicals our brain releases, not the activity or substance that brings about this release. Thus, addiction is an issue of brain functioning and our genetics significantly determine this. There's more to it.

There is robust proof to propose a genetic element to addiction. Obviously, addiction does not grow simply because a person is weak-willed. Addicted individuals do not select their genetics. And so, they do not determine whether they are at risk for having an addiction. Let me explain.

---

[1] https://www.mentalhelp.net/articles/the-many-causes-of-addiction-and-bio-psych-social-spiritual-model/

Genetics, according to empirical scientific evidence, explains 50% of whether a person will develop an addiction or not.

The studies of twins prove this. When one identical twin is an alcohol addict, there is a higher probability of the other twin being addicted as well. However, when one non-identical twin is an alcohol addict, the other twin is not necessarily addicted. Interesting, isn't it?

Based on the dissimilarities between the non-identical and identical twins, studies have shown that 50-60% of addiction is as a result of genetic factors.

Nevertheless, we are not slaves to our biology! Our behaviour is not completely driven by biological makeup. We have the capacity to choose recovery above addiction. This makes addictive disorders very analogous to other disorders and diseases. Many health issues require changes in way of life to reinstate health.

For example, people with heart disease must decide on a healthier nutrition and an exercise agenda. Clearly, these people did not elect to have these health problems. But they most definitely can decide on how to manage them. The same is true for addicts.

Based on the arguments of the biological model, each person's distinct genetics and physiology causes addiction. You might be wondering how; I will get to that in a minute.

People differ in the extent to which they enjoy or dislike a specific addictive activity or substance. Some individuals may enjoy an activity or substance so much that it becomes very alluring and tough to repulse. Another individual would not suffer this struggle because they do not feel an akin pleasure. Stay with me.

Similarly, the capacity to moderate impulsive cravings with logical thinking is a brain function that differs among various people. Some persons may be lacking in their capability to resist particular kinds of desires. Therefore, these people would be at greater risk for developing an addiction due to their genetic susceptibility.

Psychological Causes

Psychologists propose quite a few probable causes of addiction. I will try to touch on some of them.

First, individuals may participate in detrimental behaviors due to an irregularity, or "psychopathology" that exhibits itself as mental disorder.

Second, folks may acquire harmful behavior in response to their surroundings. These are addictions that are instituted by environmental elements.

Third, people's beliefs and thoughts create their state of mind. This subsequently determines their actions. To the point that a person's thoughts and views are dysfunctional or impractical, their conduct will be likewise affected.

A lot of these models have not been verified or applied to each particular kind of addiction. Nevertheless, scientists and specialists in general presume these theories apply in a certain fashion to all addictions.

The psychopathological theory perceives mental disorders as the origin of addiction. These conditions might comprise cognitive problems, mood instabilities, and other psychological disorders. In fact, addiction and other mental health conditions frequently occur together (termed co-morbidity). There's more to it.

Linked to psychopathology is the idea of an addictive persona. Specific personality attributes might be the fundamental elements in all addictive conditions. These may comprise the denial of evident problems, difficulties with regulation of emotions, and complications with desire regulation. An addiction may be a result of inability to control one's emotions and desires, as well as a blatant denial of evident problems such as a lapse in one's social connection or similar important spheres of life.

There is not enough proof to propose an "addictive personality" as such. Nonetheless, addiction most regularly co-occurs with a category of disorders known as Personality Disorders.

Negative Thinking

Negative thinking also causes addiction from a psychological, or if you will, a mental point of view. All the various forms of negative thinking let you feel strained, uncomfortable, petulant, and disgruntled.

When you think in a win-or-lose way, you consider your life as either going perfectly or horribly, you see your alternatives as either terrible or good. Emotions of this nature makes you desire to escape, unwind, or compensate yourself, which can lead to the use of substance (alcohol or drug) or an activity.

Poor Stress-Handling Skills

Here is another cause of addiction from a psychological or mental perspective. Stress is an essential risk factor in addiction. It is particularly key in the evolution from restrained drug use to needy drug abuse, from moderate indulgence in activities to total dependence on them.

Stress remains a risk factor for a number of reasons.

Firstly, the more strained you are, the more you will desire to escape or unwind, and this is the reason people turn to addictive substances—alcohol or drugs—or activities.

Secondly, when you are strained, you have a tendency to do what is well known and wrong as against what is novel and right; as a result, you are more likely to resort to your old habits and perpetuate your addiction.

Underlying Anxiety Or Depression

This is another chief mental cause of addiction. Nearly 15 to 30% of individuals with addiction are similarly victims of an underlying depression. The combination is termed a dual diagnosis.

Depression and anxiety are capable of leading to addiction. The reverse is also true. Addiction can as well cause depression and anxiety. Individuals who have a dual diagnosis frequently use alcohol, drugs and addictive activities to escape their emotions of depression and anxiety. They have a repeat pattern of remaining sober for some time and then reverting when the emotions become overpowering and they attempt to escape them.

Social-Spiritual Aspect

To complete the BPSS model, there is the socio-cultural (social) aspect which some clinicians believe includes the spiritual part although some experts want to put the spiritual aspect separately. Spiritual models presume addiction arises because of a separation from God.

From a Christian perspective for example, addiction is a sin that falls under lack of self-control and self-indulgence. I support this model, while also crediting other models as true.

People fall into addiction because, in one way or the other, they deviated from God or from His commandments. The Bible admonishes us to be temperate in all things. (2 Peter 1:6) says,

> *"And to knowledge temperance; and to temperance patience; and to patience godliness."*

It is written in (Romans 6:12),

> *"Let not sin therefore reign in your mortal body, that ye should obey it in the lusts thereof."*

Addiction negates this.

Moral causes of addiction assume there is a "correct" decency based on a specific group of values. Nonconformity to those values culminates in addiction. It is essential to note that moral codes mirror a particular cultures value system.

And so, the "correct" moral code will differ from culture to culture.

How Addiction Develops

Today, thanks to neuroimaging and ongoing research, addiction is regarded as a chronic disease that modifies both brain structure and function. It, in fact, takes over the brain. This occurs as the brain undergoes a series of alterations, starting with recognition of pleasure and culminating with a drive to compulsive actions.

All pleasures are recorded in the same manner by the brain, whether they arise with a monetary compensation, a psychoactive drug, a satiating meal, or a sexual experience. In the brain, pleasure possesses a unique signature: the discharge of the neurotransmitter dopamine in the nucleus accumbens, an assemblage of nerve cells situated below the cerebral cortex. This region of the brain is referred to as pleasure center.

Stay with me; don't bother about the technical terms. This gets interesting.

Every addictive drug, whether heroine or nicotine, gives rise to an especially potent dopamine surge in the pleasure Centre. The possibility that taking part in a rewarding activity or using a drug will culminate in addiction is directly related to the rate at which such a drug or activity enhances dopamine secretion, the intensiveness of that release, and the consistency of that release.

Meanwhile, using the same psychoactive drug via diverse administration methods can impact how likely it is to culminate in addiction. For instance, smoking or intravenous injection of a drug, as opposed to getting it down as a tablet gives rise in general to a faster, more potent dopamine indication and has greater chances of culminating in substance abuse.

I'm going to get technical again but this is a sweet part. Addictive drugs offer a shortcut of some sort to the brains reward coordination by deluging the pleasure Centre with dopamine. The hippocampus, another part of the brain, establishes memories of this swift sense of gratification, and the amygdala—another critical brain part—builds a conditioned reaction to the specific stimuli. Wait, there's more...

Before now, scientists assumed that a pleasurable experience alone was sufficient to propel folks to keep on craving an addictive activity or substance.

Recent research, however, proposes a more complicated situation. Let me explain.

Dopamine adds to the experience of pleasure, but it doesn't stop there. It takes part significantly in learning and memory—a pair of essential factors in the evolution from merely liking a thing to getting addicted to it.

Based on current addiction theory, dopamine relates with glutamate, another neurotransmitter, to hijack the brain's coordination of reward-linked learning. This coordination plays a crucial role in life sustenance since it connects activities required for human survival (e.g. eating and sex) with pleasance and compensation.

The brain's reward route comprises sections involved with stimulus and memory together with pleasure. Addictive activities and substances excite the same trail, and then surcharge it. So, what's the bottom line?

Constant exposure to an addictive behavior or attitude makes the nerve cells in the pleasure Centre and the prefrontal cortex—the brain region concerned with the planning and execution of tasks—to communicate in a manner that pairs liking a thing with craving it, successively pushing us to pursue it.

In essence, this process propels us to pursue the pleasure source. This is only halfway through addiction development. The other half comprises tolerance and compulsion. So, read on.

The brain, with time, adapts in a manner that in fact makes the craved-for activity or substance less gratifying. Naturally, rewards normally arrive only with time and exertion. Addictive behaviours and substances deliver a shortcut to this process, saturating the brain with dopamine and its likes. Our brains lack a stress-free method to endure the blitz.

For instance, habit-forming drugs can secrete 2-10 times the dopamine amount that natural compensation does, and they achieve this more swiftly and consistently. Brain receptors in an addicted person become overwhelmed. The brain reacts by secreting less dopamine or getting rid of dopamine receptors in an adaptation akin to reducing a loudspeakers volume when the noise gets too loud. Interesting, isn't it?

Due to these alterations, the impact of dopamine on the reward centre of the brain is reduced. As time passes, folks who developed an addiction usually realise that the desired activity or substance no longer provides them as much gratification. They must use/partake more of it to get the same dopamine climax since their brains have adapted, in an event called tolerance. Still with me?

Compulsion assumes control at this juncture. The pleasure connected to a habit-forming activity or substance lessens, yet the sought-after effect's memory and the need to create it again (the yearning) continues. It seems the normal motivation machinery no longer functions.

The earlier-mentioned learning process also plays a part. The amygdala and hippocampus keeps data regarding environmental signals related to the sought-after substance or activity, in order to find it again. These memories facilitate the creation of a learned response— a deep yearning—anytime the individual comes across those environmental signs.

Cravings contribute to addiction but it does even more: it also contributes to relapse after a tough abstinence. For instance, a person addicted to alcohol may be at risk of relapse upon seeing a whiskey bottle, while another individual might start to use heroin again when he sees a hypodermic needle. Condition learning facilitates the explanation of the reason folks who evolved an addiction are at the danger of backsliding even after years of sobriety.

Types Of Addictions

Addictions include substance addictions and behavioral addictions. Substance addictions include alcohol, cocaine, nicotine, hallucinogens, inhalants, opioids, caffeine, amphetamine, benzodiazepines, phencyclidine and sedatives.

While behavioral addictions include gambling, gaming, shopping, sex, eating, exercise and work. They also include other computer-related addictions such as social networking, video gaming, online gambling and cybersex.

Alcoholism

To start with, alcohol is defined as a liquor or brew containing alcohol—any of a series of volatile hydroxyl compounds that are made from hydrocarbons by distillation—as the active agent.

Alcohol is capable of intoxicating (a temporary state of imbalanced consciousness resulting from excessive consumption, and examples include wine, liquor and beer.

The word alcoholism refers to an illness called alcohol dependence syndrome, the most serious phase of a set of drinking issues which starts with binge drinking and alcohol misuse. There are different types of alcohol problems which culminates in addiction.

Types of Alcohol Issues

Alcohol problems happen at various severity levels, from mild and irritating to life-threatening. Though alcoholism (alcohol dependence) is the most serious phase, less serious dining issues can be dangerous as well. Binge drinking is a drinking problem prominent among young persons under the age of 21 and it involves simply drinking to become drunk. Officially, binge drinking comprises having five or more drinks in one sitting for men and four or more for women.

Binge drinking graduates into alcohol abuse when one's drinking starts to result in problems in one's everyday life, and the drinking remains anyway.

Put differently, alcohol abuse is when you keep on drinking regardless of sustained interpersonal, social or legal troubles. Alcohol abuse can lead to missing time at work or school, neglecting household or parental responsibilities or other issues, such as domestic violence, drunk driving or public intoxication. Since alcohol impairs your judgment, there is a higher probability of you doing something unreasonable under the influence of alcohol.

Alcohol dependence is a higher level of alcohol abuse when drinkers start to experience a longing for alcohol, a lack of control of their drinking, symptoms of withdrawal when they are not drinking and a raised tolerance to alcohol such that they must consume more to attain the same effect. Dependence on alcohol−addiction to alcohol−is a lasting and usually progressive ailment that comprises a potent need to drink regardless of repeated issues.

Alcoholism has a tendency of running in families, and a noteworthy quantity of scientific findings propose that genetics is implicated in the development of alcohol issues.

However, findings as well show that a person's surroundings and peer influences can as well influence your risk of becoming alcohol dependent. Merely having a family alcoholism history does not condemn an individual into becoming an alcoholic.

Drug Addiction

Drugs in this case are essentially narcotics. A narcotic is defined as a drug that produces numbness or stupor; often taken for pleasure or to reduce pain; extensive use can lead to addiction.

Examples include cocaine, methamphetamines, opioids such as codeine, heroin and morphine, ecstasy, cannabis (marijuana), etc.

Drug addiction is defined as a continuing, relapsing condition characterized by obsessive drug seeking and use regardless of adverse outcomes. It is regarded as a brain disease, since it consists of functional alterations to brain circuits involved in stress, reward, and self-control, and those modifications may last a protracted time after an individual has stopped using drugs.

Drug abuse is when you use legal or prohibited substances in ways you should not. This includes taking more than your prescribed dosage of drugs or use another person's prescription. Some misuse drugs to ease stress, feel good, or escape reality. But all things equal, you should be able to adjust your unhealthy habits or stop usage totally.

Addiction, on the other hand, is when you are unable to stop. Not when it puts your wellbeing at risk. Not when it results in emotional, financial, and other issues for you or your loved ones. No matter the risk, you can't just stop. That craving to obtain and use drugs can occupy your thoughts every minute, even if you wish to quit. That is addiction.

Drug addiction, like most other addictions, is a lot like other ailments, like heart disease. Both upset the usual, healthy functioning of body organs, both have severe detrimental effects, and both are, in several instances, avoidable and curable. If left untreated, however, they can linger for a lifetime and may result in death.

This brings us to why people take drugs. Generally, people use drugs for a number of reasons:

To Feel Good

Drugs are capable of producing intense pleasurable feelings. This preliminary euphoria is succeeded by other effects, which vary based on the sort of drug taken. With stimulants like cocaine, for instance, the high is succeeded by feelings of self-confidence, boosted energy and power. In contrast, the euphoria initiated by opioids like heroin is succeeded by feelings of recreation and gratification.

To Feel Better

A number of individuals who suffer from stress, social anxiety, and depression begin to use drugs in an attempt to feel less worried. Stress can play a key part in the beginning and continuous use of drug, and even relapse in patients recuperating from addiction.

Using drugs can become a method of handling painful feelings, such as loneliness, depression and anxiety, and can even worsen these issues.

To Perform Better

A number of individuals feel pressure to increase their focus at work or school or their capabilities in sports. This can make them attempt to, and continue to use, drugs like cocaine or prescription stimulants.

Social Pressure And Curiosity

In this regard, teens are chiefly at risk since peer pressure is usually strong.

Compared to adults, teens are more likely to take risks to impress their friends and display their freedom from social rules and parents.

Then comes the important question: if using drugs makes people feel good or better, what then the issue? I will get to that in a minute.

At the first instance of using a drug, individuals may feel what appear to be helpful effects. They may believe as well that they are able to regulate their use.

However, drugs can swiftly hijack a person's life. As time passes, if the use of drug persists, other enjoyable activities become less enjoyable, and the individual must use the drug to feel "normal. It becomes difficult to regulate their need to use drugs despise the several issues it causes for themselves and their loved ones.

A number of individuals begin to experience the need to use more of the drugs or use it more time and again, even in the initial phases of their use of drug. These are the revealing signs of an addiction. If the above scenario describes you, you are an addict already.

Perhaps you are beginning to wonder if people freely decide to continue taking drugs. Well, it's not a straightforward answer. Let me explain.

Typically, the preliminary choice to use drugs is voluntary. However, with constant use, the capacity of a person to exercise self-control can become severely marred; this weakening of the self-control is the mark of addiction.

Drug addiction often begins with the tentative, recreational use of drugs in social settings; but with time, it becomes more regular.

For others, specifically with opioids, exposure usually starts with recommended medications, or getting medications from a relative or friend who has been given the medication. The risk of addiction and how quick you get addicted differs by drugs. Certain drugs, such as opioid analgesics, have a greater risk and result in addiction faster than others.

Brain imaging research of addicts show alterations in the brain areas critical to decision-making, judgment, behaviour control, learning and memory. These alterations further explain the obsessive nature of addiction.

Some people become addicted to drugs and some others don't. Why, you may ask? The truth is no single element determines if an individual will become a drug addict—or not.

However, there are risk factors, the presence of which increase the likelihood that taking drugs will result in continuous use and eventual addiction. These risk factors include aggressive childhood behavior, poor social skills, lack of parental supervision, availability of drugs and drug experimentation.

Biological factors that are capable of affecting an individual's risk of addiction comprise their genetics, phase of development, and even ethnicity or gender. Scientists evaluate that genetics, including the effects environmental features have on an individual's gene expression, termed epigenetics, is responsible for between 40-60% of an individual's risk of addiction. Home and family along with school and peers represent the environmental factors that can increase the risk of addiction.

Other increasing factors of risk of addiction include early use and the method of using the drug. Even though taking drugs at any age can result in addiction, research shows that the earlier an individual starts using drugs, the more likely they are to develop severe issues. This may be as a result of the damaging effect that drugs can produce on the developing brain.

Intravenous injection or smoking of a drug enhances its addictive possibility. Both injected and smoked drugs get to the brain in a matter of seconds, creating a strong pleasure rush. This powerful high, however, can disappear in a matter of a few minutes. It is supposed that this sharply felt contrast forces a number of individuals into repeated drug use in an effort to recapture the ephemeral gratifying state.

Sexual Addiction

Like other addictions, sex addiction is a maladaptive behavioral pattern with chronic dependence on different forms of sexual expression so as to deal with the tensions of life or escape its reality. As other addictions, there is a cyclical behavioral pattern, comprising:

- Cravings and compulsions to take part in sexual activity
- A formulaic way of planning and performing sexual activity
- A sense of liberation and euphoria while taking part in the sexual activity succeeded by a withdrawal period and repeated urges.
- In essence, sexual addiction is when sex becomes a fix—when it becomes the go-to activity to deal with problems and escape reality. In this case, sex becomes like the drug in a drug addiction.

- At this point, you are probably wondering in what ways is sex addiction different from enjoying sex a lot. There is a marked difference between the two. What makes sex addiction an addiction, as against just relishing sex with many partners severally, is:

- A constant pattern of thought processes and actions, which remains regardless of damaging outcomes

- The addictive behavior lingers over a prolonged period of time

- The moment negative consequences become apparent and the addict is incapable of stopping the behavior, they have a feeling they are no longer in control.

There are several sexual behaviors ranging from the harmless to the criminal that lead to diverse outcomes, a number of which affect every person with sex addictions (e.g. relationship issues), and several of which affect less people (sexually transmitted diseases, legal problems and financial issues).

There is, however, a controversy about sex addiction for a number of reasons. Actually, there is growing proof that sex addiction follows mental and behavioral patterns, and comprises similar brain mechanisms to other addictions.

Still, sex addiction is not at present acknowledged in the Diagnostic and Statistical Manual of Mental Disorders. Though a new diagnosis of Hypersexual Disorder was suggested for DSM-V, it was not recognized.

Sex addiction is a tough concept for both professionals and the society to seriously consider. There are a number of reasons why this is so. Here are a few of them:

Unreserved recognition of sexual desire as a worldwide and enabling force is the base for sexology.

Sex encompasses an extensive and various arrays of behaviors. Some, like masturbation, are common while others, such as strange fetishes, are so unexpected and distant from "normal" behavior that others find it hard to relate to or comprehend the charm of such behavior.

Misunderstanding around what would represent "recovery" from an addiction to sex, as abstinence, the delineation of recovery for the majority of other addictions is not a sensible expectation or healthy course of action for most persons.

Since some persons with sex addictions are, in certain cases, sexually abusive to others, sex addiction can be considered as an "excuse" for abusive and irresponsible behavior.

Sex is still one of the most off-limits subjects in society, so persons with sex addictions are usually the subject of disdain and mockery in a way that individuals with other situations are not subject to.

Computer-Related Addictions

There are a range of computer-related addictions. They include internet, video and computer games, social networking sites (social media), cybersex and online gambling.

Some of these addictions are more serious than others. Most of them, including social media, online gambling and video games can, however, be subsumed under internet addictions. Let's consider internet addictions in details.

Internet addiction is a behavioral addiction in which an individual becomes reliant on use of the internet, or other online devices, as a maladaptive manner of handling life's worries. It is not yet a formally accepted mental disorder. Nonetheless, internet gaming disorder is included as an ailment for further research, and internet addiction is emerging as a specialist region.

Not less than three subtypes of internet addiction have been recognized, video game addiction, online gambling addiction, and online sex addiction or cybersex.

Gradually, addiction to mobile devices that is, smartphones and cell phones, and addiction to social media sites, such as Facebook and Instagram, are being examined. There may be intersections between each of these sub-types. For instance, online gambling consists of online games, and online games may have components of pornography.

Internet addiction may not be formally recognized but experts have been able to identify some symptoms. All kinds of Internet addiction comprise the following constituents:

Excessive Use Of The Internet

Even though the accord that disproportionate internet use is a main symptom, no one appears able to delineate precisely how much computer time passes as excessive.

While guidelines recommend no more than 120 minutes of screen time a day, this is impractical for people who use computers for study or work. A number of authors add the stipulation "for non-essential use," but for an internet addict, all computer use can feel essential.

There are couple of questions from instruments of internet addiction assessment that can help a person to assess how much is too much. If any of these conditions are happening every day, you may have an internet addiction.

How regularly do you:

- Remain online longer than you wished?
- Think or say, just a few minutes more when online?
- Hear other persons in your life whine about the amount of time you stay online?
- Conceal the amount of time you've spent online?
- Make effort and fail to reduce the time you expend online?

Withdrawal

Even though initially understood to be the basis of physical dependence on drugs or alcohol, withdrawal symptoms are now being acknowledged in behavioural addictions, internet addiction inclusive. Common internet withdrawal symptoms comprise tension, anger, and misery when internet access is not accessible. These symptoms may be seen as joylessness, boredom, nervousness, moodiness, and petulance when you can't go on the internet.

Tolerance

Tolerance is another mark of drug and alcohol addiction and appears to be related to internet addiction too. This can be assumed as wanting—and from the user's perspective, needing—more and more computer-related stimulus. It can assume numerous forms. You might only desire more time on the computer or phone, so it steadily hijacks all you do. Or you might long for more technology—bigger, improved or the most recent software, gadgets or hardware. Whichever way, the hunt for more is a principal theme in your thought processes and organization.

Negative Outcomes

If Internet addiction produces no detriment, there would be no issue. But when disproportionate computer use becomes addictive, something begins to suffer. You might not have any genuine personal relationships, or, when you do, there may suffer neglect over your use of internet.

Online affairs can grow easily and quickly, occasionally without the individual even considering online unfaithfulness as cheating on their partner.

Also, as a result of your internet use, your grades in school and other accomplishments may suffer. You may likewise have little passion for anything other than computer use. Internet addicts are usually fatigued from staying awake late on the internet and losing required sleep.

If you have a weakness for online shopping, cybersex or online gambling, finances can suffer as well.

Nicotine Addiction

Nicotine addiction is an addiction to nicotine—an alkaloid poison that occurs in tobacco. It is found in cigarettes, cigars and nicotine patches—an adhesive patch, affixed to the skin, which slowly diffuses nicotine into the bloodstream; used by people who are trying to quit smoking.

Within 7 to 10 seconds, the alkaloid in inhaled smokes of tobacco moves into the bloodstream from the lungs and up to the brain of a smoker. The moment it gets there, nicotine initiates a series of chemical reactions that produce momentary feelings of gratification for the smoker. However, these sensations are fleeting, passing off in a matter of minutes.

As the level of nicotine in the blood drops, smokers experience edginess and agitation—the beginning of nicotine withdrawal. To get rid of this uneasiness, smokers fire up another cigarette... and then one more...and another, on and on it goes—perpetuating the vicious nicotine addiction cycle. One cigarette is never sufficient, a truth every smoker is well aware of.

Nicotine triggers the same brain reward pathways that other drugs of abuse such as amphetamines or cocaine do, though to a reduced degree. Studies have shown that nicotine raises the dopamine level in the brain. The acute effects of nicotine wear thin in minutes, so smokers have to keep on dosing themselves regularly all through the day to sustain the gratifying effects of nicotine and to avert withdrawal symptoms.

Chapter 2: Signs And Symptoms Of Addiction

The symptoms of addiction will be experienced by the addicted person, while the signs will essentially be noticed by the people around them.

There are different aspects of these signs and symptoms, and they include physical, psychological and social symptoms. These effects, which manifests in symptoms and signs, are capable of significantly decreasing the quality of a person's life.

Although I have tried to categorize the symptoms in this chapter based on three prominent aspects, the reality is not so distinct. Several of these symptoms intersect and one is capable of leading to another. An instance of this overlap is when a person experiences the mental effect of desiring to divert funds meant for regular diet to buying a substance, and therefore not meeting required dietary intake. This is a compound effect of multiple symptoms of addiction.

Similarly, relationship complications and a rising loathing for social connections can result in and aggravate psychological difficulties, including anxiety and depression. In essence, one symptom can lead to another as the situation deteriorates. Lets consider each aspect of the symptoms one after the other.

Physical Symptoms

Using a substance or activity can affect an array of bodily systems and functions. Substances are chemicals that can affect the normal function of the body in different ways. The same goes for activities. These impacts manifest in different ways ranging from appetite changes to increased tolerance.

Others include withdrawal symptoms and actual diseases resulting from repeated use. The repeated use of substances or an activity can result in different impairments of the body system which manifests as diseases and ailments of varying sort and degree. Let' examine each of these physical symptoms briefly.

Withdrawal Symptoms

When there is a drop beyond a certain level in the substance or activity to which an individual has dependence, they might exhibit physical symptoms, depending on the activity or substance.

These comprise constipation, cravings, diarrhoea, sweating, seizures, trembling and strange behavior, including violence.

When an addicted person is not able to get his or her fix, they become restless and unsettled. They—their body—begin to act weird and display these withdrawal symptoms. It's as if their world is turned upside down; they are thrown into a chaotic frenzy that can only be settled by the consumption of the substance or participation in the activity on which they are dependent.

Disease Or Damage From Using A Substance

Smoking substances like crack and tobacco can result in lung cancers and incurable respiratory illnesses. Injecting proscribed drugs can result in limb damage and arterial and venous issues, in certain instances resulting in the development of infection and likely limb loss. Consuming excessive volume of alcohol regularly, for instance, can result in lasting liver problems.

The body has its normal way of functioning — and any deviation from this normal functioning results in imbalances that manifests as diseases. Too much use of any substance or activity causes these imbalances and can result in very serious life-threatening ailments. The number of people that die every year from addiction-related issues is staggering and seems to be on the increase.

Appetite Changes

Some substances change a person's desire for food. Marijuana intake, for instance, might significantly increase appetite, while cocaine may diminish it. These substances impair brain functioning and, by implication, body functioning such as the rate of hunger and the desire or need to eat.

Insomnia

Sleeplessness is a common indicator of withdrawal. The use of prohibited stimulants, such as ecstasy or speed, might similarly encourage a disordered sleep cycle, as an individual might stay up late for more than a few nights in a row to attend parties, or to enjoy the substance or activity to which they are addicted.

Addicts usually use these substances at night. They sometimes do this to conceal their use from others. This, as you can imagine, prevents them from having enough sleep—a situation that can lead to bigger health problems down the road.

Growing Tolerance

The body witnesses lessened effects of the substance with the passage of time, so a person experiences the need to consume more to realise the same effect. This is what is otherwise known as behavioral adaptation. The human body is capable of learning and memory. If a person takes little portions of poison every day, they will become resistant to the poison over time. If a person uses a substance or activity repeatedly, their body will get used to it and normalize the process by increasing their tolerance. This means that a person's threshold adjusts based on consistent use.

If a person starts smoking three cigarettes per day, at first they will feel the heightened effects of the nicotine for a while. But with the passage of time, their body will adjust and see the three cigarettes as normal which means the effects of the three sticks become significantly lessened. To achieve the initial effect of smoking three sticks, the person now has to graduate to five, and on it will continue.

A Change In Look

A person may start to look more tired, disheveled, and exhausted, as indulging in their addiction could take a significant portion of the day, leaving little or no time for necessities like exercising, attending to personal hygiene and washing clothes.

The person might also remain indoor for a long time, not bothering to take care of their appearance such that they don't change their clothes or even brush their teeth. They are rather preoccupied with the addictive substance or activity; every other thing becomes secondary!

A person might exhibit a few of these symptoms or several of them depending on the type of substance or activity to which they are addicted and the extent of addiction. Substance use syndrome can have a hugely different effect on each individual.

Social Symptoms

Addiction can affect how a person mixes with and relates to other folks. Although social issues can lead to addiction, the reverse is much more likely. Addiction is capable or ruining social connections and even prevent them as well. An addict faces many social hurdles which they might be unable to scale.

Forgoing Human Contact

An individual with activity or substance dependence might pass on certain undertakings that brought them satisfaction in the past. For instance, an individual dependent on nicotine may decide not to hang out with friends if they have a plan to head out to a smoke-free restaurant or pub. Similarly, an alcohol addict may pass on an invitation to spend the day on a boat, in a park or camping, in the absence of alcohol.

This also applies to activities, or if you may, behaviors. An addict will sacrifice otherwise satisfying actions simply because they don't promise the satisfaction that they will get from their fix. In essence, addicts miss out on the opportunity to form or strengthen social connections because of their addiction. They decline otherwise valuable social events because it doesn't guarantee them the availability of their fix—that soothing release of dopamine.

Secrecy And Isolation

In numerous instances, an individual with an addiction may use the substance on their own or carry out the activity in secret. Since some or most of the things—activities and substances—to which a lot of people are addicted are things not approved by their friends, parents, siblings and family, or even considered lawful by the society, most addicts resort to using them in secret only, away from the prying eyes of others.

Addicts are thus usually isolated, secluded and, especially, secretive to avoid getting caught and having to face the embarrassment or punishment that comes with being found out.

Cutting Out Of Hobbies

As an addiction advances, the person may stop participating in hobbies they hitherto relish. Folks who are hooked on tobacco, for instance, might discover they can't physically handle participating in their favourite sport any longer.

Addiction leads people to stop participating in the things they love as the addictions are either directly against their hobby (the rules of a sport for example) or impairs their body functions such that they can no longer participate in their hobbies.

Denial

A noteworthy amount of people with addiction do not realize that they have an issue. They might realize their physical dependence on an activity or a substance but deny —refuse to admit —the need to go for treatment, being certain that they can stop "anytime" they desire to.

Most addicts live under the illusion that they can handle their addictions with will power which is, in fact, false. They deny that they are addicted and lie to themselves that they are in charge and can easily put an end to consuming the stimulating substance or taking part in the satisfying activity.

Sustaining A Steady Supply

People with chemical/substance addiction will always ensure they have a rich supply, even if they do not possess much money. They may cut some things off their home budget to guarantee the availability of the stimulating chemical or substance. Addicts will go to any length to maintain a steady supply of their fix, because to them, their life depends on it. They will not hesitate to do dangerous or irrational things just to make sure they don't run out of their dopamine-supplying substance.

Keeping Stashes

An individual with an addiction may possess small stashes of a substance secretly stored in various parts of the car or house, usually in places one won't expect, to escape being found out.

They safeguard these stashes so that they can easily retrieve them in the event that they need to get high later. It is their way of preparing for the "rainy day".

Abuse Or Excess Consumption Of Substances

Certain kinds of addiction, such as opiate or alcohol use disorders, can make a person to take unsafe quantities of a substance. Abusing a substance can have severe physical effects, including overdosing.

However, for an individual with substance addiction, these effects will not be sufficient to avert future abuse.

In a bid to keep the juices (dopamine and co) flowing in their brain, addicts go overboard with the abuse of the stimulating substance or activity; they consume more than their body can take. This can lead to dangerous conditions such as loss of consciousness, sanity or even loss of life in extreme instances, in the case of substance abuse.

Financial Problems

A costly substance can result in considerable and consistent financial sacrifices to guarantee a steady supply. This is a secondary symptom. In trying not to run out of the stimulant(s), addicts might spend all that they have on procuring substances, which results in all sorts of financial problems. This can even lead to other secondary crimes such as stealing and fraud just to ensure that they have enough money to buy their fix.

Legal Difficulties

This is typical of unlawful drug and alcohol dependences. Legal difficulties may come about either because the substance mars judgment, and thus leads the person to undertake risks to the point of instigating violence or public disorder, or flouting the law to obtain the substance in the beginning.

Psychological Symptoms

Addiction symptoms that result in mental disorders comprise the following:

A Lack Of Ability To Halt Usage

In several instances, like dependence on alcohol, nicotine or other stuff, an individual will have tried unsuccessfully—at least once—to quit the addiction.

This might be physiological as well, as certain substances, take heroin for example, are chemically addictive. If an individual stops taking them, it results in withdrawal symptoms. An addict soon finds out that they lack the ability to break their addiction.

To paraphrase Soren Kierkegaard, they discover that the chains of habits are too weak to be felt until they are strong to be broken.

Handling Problems

An individual with addiction usually feels the need to carry out the addictive activity or take the implicating substance to handle their problems. Instead of facing their problems and meeting them head on, addicts resolve to using their addiction to handle their problems.

Taking An Opening Large Dose

This is typical with alcohol addiction. The person may quickly drink large volumes of alcohol so as to experience the effects and feel good. In order to feel that spurt of dopamine, they result to taking an initial large dose.

Continued Use And Abuse Despite Health Difficulties

The person continues to take the substance or carry out the activity regularly, although they now have related diseases or sicknesses.

For instance, a smoker may keep on smoking after even developing a heart or lung disease. They may or may not know of the health effect of the activity or substance, yet they continue to indulge in it.

Obsession

An individual may become fixated on a substance, expending more and more energy and time seeking ways of obtaining their substance, and in some instances the way they can use it. They are always looking for novel ways to enjoy the activity or substance to which they are addicted. For example, if they snuff the substance, they might consider injecting it for greater and maximum effect.

Taking Risks

A person with an addiction may take risks to engage in the activity or get the substance, such as stealing or swapping sex for prohibited drugs, alcohol, and cash for drugs/alcohol. While still feeling the effect of certain substances, an individual with substance use syndrome may take part in risky undertakings, such as fast and precarious driving or even violence.

Addiction has several symptoms that can result in damage to a person's psychological or physical health, social life and daily activities. The effects are heavily dependent on the sort of substance or activity, personal conditions, family life, an individual's awareness of their behaviours and their current financial state.

Psychologically, an addiction is capable of resulting in continued use in spite of other effects on health and a lack of ability to halt usage. A person might be preoccupied with finding a substance or participating in their detrimental activities.

Substance and habit-forming behaviors might likewise result in a pulling out from personal duties, formerly essential activities, and social connections. They may cause a person to pursue solitude and take part in the habituated use of substance in secret.

Addiction can as well result in clashes with the law, both in procuring a substance and carrying out unusual or messy actions that stem from substance use.

Taking a substance regularly can likewise result in physical injury, depending on the sort of drug. Some substances result in withdrawal symptoms that comprise several physical effects, such as sweating, shaking, nausea or diarrhoea.

If you or someone you know exhibits any of these symptoms, you should consider treatment for yourself or the individual you are worried about, as quickly as possible.

Chapter 3: Effects Of Addiction

Addiction—of any kind—can lead to an extensive range of problems that impact personal relationships, professional goals, and overall health. With the passage of time, these severe side effects can be progressive, and fatal if left untreated.

In essence, addiction is capable of turning a person's entire life upside down, and even kill the person. Thousands of people die every year all over the world from addiction and related issues.

It is the nature of the brain to make you desire to repeat experiences that make you feel good. You're driven, as a result, to do them over and over again.

Anything that may be addictive, be it substances such as drugs and alcohol or behaviors such as sex or online gaming, targets the reward system of your brain. They overflow your brain with a chemical (a neurotransmitter) called dopamine.

This activates a feeling of deep gratification so that you keep taking the substance or perform that activity to pursue that high.

As time goes on, your brain becomes used to the extra dopamine. Therefore, you might be required to take more of the substance or do more of the activity to experience the same good feeling.

What's more, other things you delight in, like food and spending time with family and friends, may give you less satisfaction.

When you use addictive substances such as drugs for a protracted time, it can lead to alterations in other brain chemical circuits and systems as well. They can upset your:

- Judgment
- Decision making
- Memory
- Stress
- Behaviour
- Ability to learn

The effects of these upsets are far-reaching such that they are arguably limitless. When your decision making, for instance, is impaired, you do things that you will not ordinarily do. You make decisions that are not especially rational or appropriate. For example, excessive consumption of alcohol as a result of addiction can lead to publicly disgraceful behaviours that can result in all forms of problems.

Substance addiction, i.e. drug and alcohol addiction, have many adverse medical effects which include, but is not limited to:

Cardiovascular Disease

- Changes in body temperature, appetite and sleeping patterns
- Heart rate irregularities, heart attack
- Constipation, vomiting, diarrhoea, abdominal pain
- Respiratory problems such as emphysema, lung cancer, and breathing problems
- Liver and kidney damage

- Pancreatitis
- Brain damage, seizures, stroke,
- Gastrointestinal complications
- Insomnia and sleep disorders
- Malnutrition

Any and all of these disorders could become life-threatening. More so, they are usually overlapping in their occurrence, which may lead to death in extreme cases.

The effects of addiction are not only biological/medical, they can also be mental or social just like the causes and symptoms.

Among the mental effects of addiction are the twin disorders of depression and loneliness. These mental health disorders can lead to or result from addiction. In essence, as I've mentioned earlier, they are capable of causing addiction. They can equally be caused by addiction.

Loneliness can result from addiction in that the addict suffers from several social connection problems due to a compulsive use and dependence on certain activities and substance. Similarly, problems arising from addiction can push a person into the dreary pit of depression.

A major effect of addiction is spending less time on activities that used to be important, such as hanging out with family and friends, exercising, or pursuing hobbies or other interests. This is a significant effect. When a person becomes addicted to a substance or to an activity, other important activities become secondary while the addiction becomes primary.

What this means is that an addict become less interested in other things or parts of their life as his or her addiction comes first regardless of whether there are negative consequences or not. Less and less attention is paid to other activities, even one as important as personal hygiene.

This new imbalance leads to a lot of other imbalances in the life of the addict, thereby subsequently making life more difficult for them. What is worse is that when these attendant problems begin to show up, the addict runs to the addiction to serve as a way to escape reality, hence worsening the problem and continuing the vicious cycle until their life is a total mess.

Drop in attendance and performance in school or at work is another prominent effect of addiction.

Since addiction has the tendency to be time-consuming and hijack thought processes and systems, addicts begin to lose concentration little by little. They are unable to focus on anything due to largely divided attention. This starts to lead to negatives outcomes at work if the addict works in an organisation, or poor grades if the addict is a student. They are unable to focus on a task, an assignment, a class or even a project. They go to work or school late, and forget to fulfil their responsibilities because they are busy going after the juice in their brain. They can't think straight, and making the right decisions becomes an uphill task.

Addiction prevents the victim from preparing for a test, an exam or a presentation. Addiction does not only hijack the addict's mental processes, it steals their time as well as their sleep—a combination that is certain to lead to more and more negative outcomes down the road. This is the summary of how addiction truncates professional goals, ambition and aspirations.

Another notable effect of addiction is taking severe risks in order to get one's substance or activity of choice. In general, most addictive substances are rare and expensive since they are mostly proscribed substances. This doesn't deter addicts though. Once they are hooked, addicts will go to great lengths just to acquire their fix.

These may include engaging in all sorts of criminal activity which may include, but is not limited to stealing, extortion, prostitution, street-begging and even murder in extreme cases. To sustain their steady supply of the addictive substance, addicts sometimes engage in dangerous and risky activities. Folks can go about begging on the street or even prostitution (in the case of females) just to get enough money to get the substance to which they are addicted. Addicts won't hesitate to take these risks as they are no longer in control of themselves. They pander easily to anything that will guarantee that their cravings are satisfied. This can also make them ready tools in the hands of those who have criminal motives. Such criminals will commission addicts on dangerous jobs in exchange for a dosage of their fix.

Also included in the effects of addiction is acting out in personal relationships, especially if someone is trying to address an addict's substance or activity problems. One of the greatly affected parts of an addict's life is social connections. Making and sustaining social connections become a difficult task for addicts. The reason is not far-fetched. They are busy using a substance or indulging in an activity. When they are not doing this, they are busy thinking about how to acquire the substance or how best to use it.

Or they are preoccupied with thoughts of getting or actually seeking resources that will enable them participate in that activity to which they are addicted. This makes it difficult for addicts to maintain any decent personal relationships: they have limited time, efforts and resources to put in the relationship. For those that are in relationships before they developed an addiction, addiction makes it difficult to sustain the relationship. Soon enough, such relationships will deteriorate and eventually break up.

This brings us to financial woes and legal troubles. Addicts tend to spend as much as they can to ensure that they keep getting their fix. For instance, online gambling addicts might continue to spend their money gambling until they are essentially bankrupt. The same goes for alcohol and drug addicts who continue to make reckless financial commitments just to keep getting high on their preferred substance. Addicts also find themselves breaking societal laws and regulations in order to satisfy their cravings. This might lead to all sort of legal issues that can result in significant fines or jail time. Many people are behind bars for using prohibited drugs and from committing criminal acts under the influence of several harmful addictive substances ranging from alcohol to narcotics.

In extreme cases, all these effects—medical, mental and social—combine to lead to death. The death may result directly from any of the addiction, or an addiction-related issue. A person may die from drink-driving, lung cancer, respiratory diseases, stroke or liver problems, all of which are possible effects of addiction.

From a spiritual point of view, addiction has and continues to ruin a lot of destinies. There are many souls out there who are destined for greater things but have lost their glories to the abysmal pit of addiction where they keep falling deeper by the day. Time and again, I meet young men and women who should be doing exploits in different fields and endeavours but are trapped in one addiction or the other. They have lost their identity, for the devil has derailed them by luring them into all forms of addiction.

Addiction prevents you from seeing your potential, what you are capable of and what you can become. It greatly limits people's thinking and consigns them to a life of mediocrity or dependence.

Addicts are narrow minded; they think mostly about getting the next dose, and then the next.

Today, a lot of men and women are lost in the maze and vicious cycle of addiction. These are individuals that should be making strides in ministry, business, academics, arts and science and technology.

They are instead neck-deep in every form of addiction out there. They are drinking and smoking away at nightclubs and in their closets. They are glued to their phone and laptop screens clicking away on the internet. Their lofty ambitions and goals have been squashed by the constant longing for that dopamine rush. They cannot see beyond the next dose of their fix. They are in a rut!

Addiction can also be the basis for certain people's shocking fall from grace to grass. Many individuals have been relieved of their roles in establishments, institutions and governments because of addiction.

Several careers, businesses and ministries have come crashing down because of dependence on a substance or an activity. Due to their inability to tame their cravings, many people have gone from wealth to poverty—from the mansion to the streets. Several people have gone from VIP to nonentity. Many men and women of God have fallen to disrepute and ridicule because of addiction.

What's worse, the effects of addiction transcend the personal or individual level. It affects the family, then the community and eventually the nation as a whole. In some parts of the world, certain addictions are now considered national issues requiring urgent attention.

When a father or mother is addicted to a substance, for example, it may lead to a dysfunctional family whereby the children suffer from lack of parental supervision and other related issues. This negligence on the part of the parent might also lead the children to addiction such as gaming—video and online, gambling, sex and even drugs thereby leading to a dangerous cycle that can continue for generations.

When a child is addicted, he/she can also influence the siblings who then pick up the same addiction until it becomes a serious issue for the family to deal with.

Much as parents can influence children to become addicts, the opposite too might happen although that's less common.

Apart from that, an addicted parent may affect their child(ren) in other ways. Lack of enough attention from the parent may lead the child(ren) to other sorts of vices, most of which are criminal. It can as well lead to a troubled childhood which metamorphose into an even more troubled adulthood as the individual grows.

When a mother, father or child is in the firm grasp of addiction, he/she can influence their friends who can in turn influence their other friends.

If this continues, addiction becomes a communal problem, affecting a significant portion of a community's population. This can lead to a chain of events, including a growing poor culture, a dysfunctional society and sick citizenry of the said community.

The characteristics of such communities are increased crime rate and mortality rate as well as decreased productivity and prosperity. Such a society is headed for doom and gloom unless something drastic is done to halt and reverse the addiction trend.

If it's not curbed at the community level, addiction can filter into the fibre of an entire nation. The same problems—increased crime rate and mortality rate as well as decreased productivity and prosperity— from the community level applies but on a much bigger scale that will take significant time to eliminate.

The good news is that addiction can be treated and ☐cured☐. An addict can become clean again, although it requires some serious and demanding work.

But before we consider how one can stop their addiction and attain full recovery, there is something we must know. In the next chapter, we will try to see why addiction is spreading like wildfire in harmattan. Keep reading, there's more insight on the critical subject of addiction to come in the remaining parts of this book.

Why Is Addiction Spreading Like Wildfire In Harmattan?

More and more people are getting addicted to one substance/activity or another by the day. Nowadays, almost everyone you meet or know—friends, family members, colleagues, partners—is addicted either to a substance or an activity or even both in some serious cases.

One begins to wonder why this is so. Why are so many people falling into this abysmal pit?

As a matter of fact, there are many reasons addiction seems to be on the increase. I will dwell on a few of them in this chapter.

Lack Of Parental Supervision

Most teens fall into addiction as a result of lack of (enough) parental supervision. A significant percentage of addicts fall within this age group or started using the substance or activity from this stage of their lives. Since the brain is still actively undergoing changes at this stage, addictions tend to alter the brain functions at this stage, and the resultant modified brain may remain like that into and throughout adulthood. It is a worrying truth.

Adolescence is an important transitional period in every person's life. It is largely and usually a period of experimentation for most people. It often tends to be a period of rebellion when young persons who are just growing into adults want to show to their friends and anybody who cares to know that they are now independent of their parents and social rules/values. They want to come off as adults who can now do anything they like, often not realising the gravity or future implications of majority of their actions.

In this restless search for liberty and adventure, most teenagers stumble on alcohol, drugs and all sorts of addictive activities as well. This may be through friends, their own personal discovery or even through unwitting parents.

Thanks to the internet, everything ranging from information to retail outlets where one can obtain all kinds of materials is now within reach. So, the adolescent voluntarily starts to use these substances or activities. They may use them for recreational purposes, to ease stress and tension and to occasionally escape reality. This is when parental supervision should come in as an intervention to prevent addiction, to stop the gradual graduation of occasional use into a full-blown dependence.

In a proper family where the home is based on correct principles and the parents are really concerned about their children, the parents will soon find out that their ward has started using substances or activities capable of leading to addiction.

With wisdom and love, parents are able to relate to their children, showing them the dangers of using addictive substances and activities. They are able to advise their children, lead them aright and prevent them from addiction.

But because most parents have little or no time for their children these days, there is no one to put the young people right, which allows to widespread addiction. Parents are rather busy running after their careers and some of them their personal vices such that they have no time to look after their children. It is worse when the child picks the addiction from one or both of the parents.

This is the prevalent situation today. A lot of parents are not as concerned about their children as they should be. Many people were not ready to raise a family when they jumped into it. Although one can never be fully ready for parenting, most people in today's world are not even ready to put in the requisite work to raise a family. Once they encounter any little obstacle, they cave in under the pressure and leave their children to suffer. And this is one of the chief reasons addiction is spreading like wildfire in harmattan.

When parents instruct their children by affirming them and sincerely and regularly communicating their belief in them— specifically teenagers who are undergoing their second identity crisis, they can easily save them from addiction and even achieve other incalculable and amazing positive results.

Peer Pressure

In the history of humanity, I'm not sure there has been a time in which the desire to "feel among and look cool too" has been as pronounced as this.

In today's world, more people have an external point of loci and they seek validation from other people. To get this validation, they subscribe to activities that make them socially acceptable to a particular group or clique. In a number of cases, these activities are those that lead to addiction. They range from substance use to all forms of sex and internet addiction.

No thanks to the internet, the desire to measure up has never been this pronounced. Only so few people have the self-control and guts to be the odd one out. Only so few people can resist joining the bandwagon. More than before, people now want to belong. They want to be a part of the trendy people, they want to have a place too amongst the bad guys and in exclusive circles. This is what leads most people to addiction.

Most addicts are introduced to the addictive substance or activity by their peers, and this cuts across all ages. It is a reality in both teenage and adult circles.

For example, in a group of four friends, only two might be alcoholics at first. These two persuade their friends to start drinking too. In the beginning, the friends might say no and wave off the overtures of their addicted buddies. But when they hang out together, the alcoholics may make fun of the other two for drinking soda or water. One bottle won't kill you, they may say to their friends. They might even offer to buy the alcohol for them. Over time, the two non-drinkers may eventually agree to take a bottle—just one bottle, then they start taking two bottles, then three until they become alcoholics themselves.

The exact same scenario could play out for other addictions such as drugs and even activities like gaming or sex. One place where peer pressure really comes to the fore is in the development of addictions.

Initially, the clean individual is being persuaded by their addicted peers to start using the addictive substance or activity. At first, this might most likely be met with significant resistance from the clean person. But with time, after series of jests and other subtle methods of persuasion (such as coaxing) and pressuring, the clean person will try out the addictive substance or activity, and eventually become an addict themselves. It is a gradual—slow and steady—process that can take months, but usually it culminates in pressuring of the clean person into the addiction.

For teenagers, they are pressured by their peers who may or may not be their friends into almost every type of addiction, including drugs, sex, online gaming, social media, online gambling, etc.

For adults, they are usually pressured into drinking (alcohol) and smoking (nicotine).

Peer pressure in all its forms and guises without a doubt accounts for the wide spread of addiction in recent times.

Lack Of Moral And Spiritual Character

We now live in a world in which only a few people have moral fibre and spiritual uprightness. Most people in the world now do not have a strong core that is based on correct principles.

Many a person now think morality is needless or too burdensome, and that being temperate is not especially a virtue. Most people do not consider self-restraint and moderation as proper virtues. As such they do not regard immoderation and lack of self-control as unbecoming vices. What this means is that a good number of people do not have a solid inner core that can prevent them from falling into addiction.

Most religions consider immoderation of any sort a reprehensible vice, as an action that is not befitting of any faithful person. Addiction is regarded in most, if not all, religious and moral tenets as a corruption of the soul and a defilement of the body. It is seen as a moral perversion—an impairment of virtue and moral principles—because it results from a lack of discipline.

Addiction hijacks a person's life because they lack moral authority. Dependence on a substance or activity is in essence wrong when observed through a moral lens or from a spiritual perspective.

It is a form of indulgence, sacrificing what matters most (good health, moral uprightness) in life for the thrill or pleasure of the moment. But today, most people have decided to shun morality and religious uprightness in the illusory pursuit of what may be called absolute liberty.

More and more people want to live their lives without any regard for their mental and physical health or even spiritual wellbeing. More and more individuals do not care about the long-term effects of becoming an addict until it is too late.

The absence of correct principles as the core in most people's lives means anything goes. When such people are offered addictive substances and/or asked to participate in addictive activities, they are unable to say no, because they have neither moral fibre nor a system to restrain themselves before they become addicted.

A lack of character is one that could largely be caused by nurture—that is, upbringing. Most people end up not living their lives according to proper principles and values as a result of their upbringing.

Our attitudes stem from our paradigms, perceptions and centre which are scripted over time, by our experiences. The foundation for these paradigms are usually laid during childhood and carried into adulthood. A person's worldview is largely influenced by how they have been conditioned to see the world from childhood.

After all, we don't see the world as it is, but as we are, or as we are conditioned to see it due to our experience. A poor childhood, usually resulting from a lack of proper parental care, instruction and supervision, can lead to adults who have no moral character, and as such can fall easily to addictions.

A lack of moral fibre can also stem from the type of environment in which a person is brought up. An environment where good values are not promoted mostly produce individuals who have little to no proper principles by which they live their life.

Even though nurture and even genetics can largely influence what a person will become, the ultimate decisive factor is still choice. As hard as it is to accept, the fundamental truth is that human beings are a product of their choices.

We have been endowed with self-awareness, imagination, conscience and independent will. The first and last of these endowments ensure that we can decide who we want to become and what we want to do per time.

It takes discipline, which is a conscious choice, to shun addiction. It is safe to say then that addiction is spreading rapidly because more and more people are choosing to jettison morality and temperance in the pursuit of short-lived gratification and fun.

More and more individuals are choosing the path of least resistance, embracing that which is easy. A lot of folks are becoming hedonic—devoted to pleasure, while every other thing comes second.

From a Christian perspective, more individuals are becoming less and less concerned about the kingdom of God and being a citizen of the glorious eternal kingdom. The fear of God and attendant obedience to His commandments do not mean anything to more and more persons by the day.

Just like in the days of Noah, people are deep in sin and rebellion against God. They dismiss the Bible, the living word of God, as a storybook and go about their life with wantonness. "There is no God," they say to themselves, as they follow the path of Sodom and Gomorrah to destruction.

Lack of self-control which results in addiction is a work of the flesh that will continue to manifest in different forms until the flesh is conquered and put under the control of the Holy Spirit.

When the old things are yet to pass away to make way for the new in Christ, addiction will easily encroach on a person's life. So, one reason addiction is on the rise is this: people refuse to surrender themselves to the only God that is truly capable of saving them.

People are falling into the bottomless pits of addiction on a daily basis because they are not putting their strength in the eternal rock of ages, but are relying on their will, which isn't strong enough, to conquer the wiles of substance and activity dependence. Addiction is a fundamental problem that won't have its way when there is an earlier fundamental basis in Christ.

An Increasing Desire To Escape Reality

Due to a combination of the factors above and greater ease of access to addictive substances and activities, more and more people just opt to escape reality when presented with a life problem.

Take the ease of accessing the internet, for example, an increasing number of individuals can now gamble, play video games or watch pornography online without going through too much trouble. All it takes is typing in a web address and hitting a button.

When faced with difficulties of any form in life such as loss (of a job, relationship or loved one), instead of tackling the problem head on, a growing number of individuals just resort to the use of addictive substances and activities. They do this because participating in and using the activities and substances respectively help them to forget their problems, if only for a while.

These indulgences help to numb their feelings of pain temporarily. For some time, they have nothing to worry about as they revel in the rush of dopamine in their brain. It helps them suspend the immediate need to attend to their worries. At that point, things seems just perfect for the person.

But then, the feelings of "highness" created by the substance or activity is fleeting. It doesn't last forever; it wears off within a short while. This brings the person crashing down back into reality, against their very wish.

Interestingly, at this point, reality seems even harder than it actually is or initially was. The reason being that they are coming from an inflated high back to the ground; they are being hurled hard to face the brutal facts of reality.

More often than not, the individual finds it hard to deal with the reality they once ran away from. So what do they do? They simply go for another dose of the substance or activity to sustain the dopamine rush and suspend reality still. And so the vicious cycle continues until they are terribly hooked.

All the highlighted reasons for the current prevalence of addiction are all related and one always leads to another. As much as they each facilitate the occurrence of addiction, they are also connected. This is why to treat and cure addiction demands a holistic, comprehensive approach.

Chapter 4: Road To Recovery From Addiction

Ascertaining whether you have addiction isn't entirely straightforward.

More so, admitting it is not particularly easy, mainly due to the shame and stigma linked with addiction. Nonetheless, conceding the problem is the first step in the direction of recovery.

A "yes" response to any of these three questions suggests you might have an issue with addiction and had better—at the very least—turn to a health care provider for additional assessment and guidance:

- Do you participate in the behavior or use more of the substance more often than in the past?
- Do you experience withdrawal symptoms when you don't engage in the behaviour or use the substance?

- Have you ever lied to anyone regarding your extent of your behaviour or use of the substance?

I earlier mentioned that the precise cause of addiction is uncertain. It follows that a lack of agreement exists as well about the approach to treatment that is most effective.

One of the controversial issues on the causes and even treatment of addiction is that of personal responsibility. It is worthwhile to mention that this issue is not peculiar to addictive conditions.

Folks who develop hypertension and heart disease due to obesity face difficulties that are similar. The same applies to cigarette-smoking cancer patients.

What every patient has in common is that the ailment is as a result of lifestyle preferences—things we can control. Other parts of these ailments are as a result of genetics—things we have no control over.

This leads to a problem regarding personality responsibility.

Who is the cause of the problem? Who ought to find a solution to the problem?

These two questions give rise to four possibilities regarding responsibility for personal issues. These four possibilities include the moral, medical, enlightenment/spiritual and compensatory models.

The Moral Model

Folks are responsible for creating and finding solutions to their own problems.

The Enlightenment Model

People are responsible for creating, but not finding solutions to their own problems.

The Medical Model

Individuals are neither responsible for creating nor solving their own problems.

The Compensatory Model

Folks are responsible for solving, but not creating, their own problems.

However, to address the road to recovery from addiction, it is important that we first recognise the importance of locus of control.

Locus Of Control/Personal Responsibility

This subject of personal responsibility for difficulties and their solutions thrusts deeper fundamental issues to the fore. Specifically, it shows whether we consider ourselves as the director, or the actor, of our own lives.

In the course of this book, I have proposed that every individual has a freedom to select from the diverse hypothetical addiction models. Preferably, individuals in recovery will select some aggregation of the models that best suit their circumstances and needs. Through this technique, they can find a solution to their addiction issues.

These choices, however, are greatly controlled by a steady personality characteristic referred to as "locus of control".

In simple words, this personality feature describes an individual's sense of control over their own lives. People's comprehension of their ability to direct their own lives will significantly determine which kinds of recovery frameworks are most appropriate for them.

As for people who possess an internal locus of control, they believe they will define their own futures as a result of their own activities or deeds. Supposing life is a kind of theatrical display, these individuals would regard themselves as the directors in charge of their own lives.

On the other hand, when individuals possess an external locus of control, they do not believe they have power over what their future looks like. As far as they are concerned, things just befall them. They believe they possess no influence or power over their lives. To use the same analogy of life being a theatrical performance, these individuals would regard themselves as "ordinary actors", or worse, spectators, in their own lives.

Locus of control is simply the sense of control people have over their lives. It also delineates the way individuals comprehend the difficulties they encounter.

In a related fashion, it predicts to a certain degree the way they will endeavour to find a solution to these issues. For instance, if a person has an internal locus of control, they suppose problems are their own doing (after all, they are in charge of their life). They also suppose that they must find a solution to their own issues (since they created them).

Like most personality features, locus of control is a fairly constant and enduring facet of personality. It is so unchanging that we forget that it's there. We are not aware of how our peculiar locus of control influences our comprehension of an issue.

Nevertheless, it significantly influences our method of tackling problems. It is possible for locus of control to change, but it changes bit by bit, over several years.

Given the stability of locus of control and the way it affects our approach to issues, it becomes exceedingly relevant to addiction recovery. A recovery approach that does not agree with your own locus of control will most likely fail.

Thus, you must discover or create a recovery approach that best syncs with your own place on the locus of control scale (stretching from external to internal). There is a standard test that you can take to determine your locus of control. You can take it here2.

Or you can determine this even more simply by assessing your own approaches toward recovery from addiction.

Do you consider yourself an individual that must find a solution to your addiction issue?

---

[2] http://www.psych.uncc.edu/pagoolka/LocusofControl-intro.html

Or, do you consider the solution principally emerging from other people?

You will be more comfortable with a moral model or a compensatory model if you possess a robust internal locus of control.

On the other hand, you will certainly resonate with medical model or an enlightenment model if you possess a robust external locus of control. You might be wondering what these models are, do not worry. I will get to them in detail shortly.

These acute discrepancies between an external and internal locus of control assists us in defining this personality aspect.

That being said, no individual displays an absolute external or internal locus of control. The majority of us tilt to one bearing or the other. The important thing is to identify to which bearing you are tilting. By so doing, you can more effortlessly align your recovery endeavours to your own character and inclinations.

Spiritual/Enlightenment Model Of Addiction And Recovery Implications

This idea of this model is "I'm responsible for creating the problem, but I'm not responsible for solving it." It identifies that what is needed to solve the problem, addiction in this case, is self-discipline.

The healthy recovery application of this model is based on looking back to identify the causes of one's addiction and learning from one's mistakes. It's in saying "I'm going to follow the direction and guidance of a greater power that can show me how to transform my life–completely, if needed□.

Based on the spiritual model of addiction, a disconnection from the almighty God or a higher power results in addiction.

If you remember, we mentioned this under the causes of addiction in the BPSS model earlier in the book. This separation from God causes people to suffer because they do not live according to the direction or will of God. In this case, recovery comprises instituting or re-instituting a connection with the almighty God or a higher power. It involves going back to the source, returning to the base and surrendering power to the one who has all the power in the world.

When you return to Christ Jesus, you become a new creation. The Bible says in (2 Corinthians 5:17-19),

Therefore if any man be in Christ, he is a new creature: old things are passed away; behold, all things are become new. And all things are of God, who hath reconciled us to himself by Jesus Christ, and hath given to us the ministry of reconciliation; To wit, that God was in Christ, reconciling the world unto himself, not imputing their trespasses unto them; and hath committed unto us the word of reconciliation."

When you surrender power back to the Most High, you are reconciled to him and He can help you overcome your frailties, addiction inclusive.

When you become a child of God, as written in (John 1:12-13),

"But as many as received him, to them gave he power to become the sons of God, even to them that believe on his name: Which were born, not of blood, nor of the will of the flesh, nor of the will of man, but of God"

You gain power over all forms of weaknesses, including addiction, and become an ambassador of Christ. What this means is that you exercise power over your spirit, soul and body by virtue of your righteousness in God.

(2 Corinthians 5:20) says,

"Now then we are ambassadors for Christ, as though God did beseech you by us: we

pray you in Christ's stead, be ye reconciled to God."

As ambassadors of Christ, we gain authority over our weaknesses and lapses as we assume the righteousness of God.

When we reconnect with God, we start on a path to recovery from addiction. The spiritual approach to dealing with addiction is the most potent because after all, we are spiritual beings.

To paraphrase Teilhard de Chardin, We are not human beings having a spiritual experience, we are spiritual beings having a human experience.

All other parts of the human being is directly influenced by the spiritual. The spiritual aspect of the human being that aspires to a higher power, to God, supersedes and directs the mental, emotional and physical aspect of a person.

A real connection to the spiritual leads to significant changes in a person's life. These changes are capable of setting a person on the path to recovery from addiction.

First, there will be a paradigm shift that will result in a fundamental change of character. This new development will filter into the mental and emotional spheres and finally distil into the behavioral transformations. This is the recovery implication of the spiritual model.

A prominent case of the spiritual approach to recovery from addiction is Alcoholics Anonymous (AA) and other 12-step assemblies such as Cocaine Anonymous and Narcotics Anonymous. This is a free treatment program for folks who are victims of alcohol abuse and addiction.

Participants in these groups practice 12 steps to attain and maintain abstinence from alcohol. Many people use a sponsor to assist them through the process.

The group uses a spiritual approach that comprises a conviction in a higher power. Members delineate that higher power as they choose—it does not necessarily have to be God. The group usually hold meetings in public settings such as schools or churches. Certain meetings are open to anyone who is interested while others are only for alcoholics or potential AA members. Joining the group is free, the only condition being a desire to stop drinking. To join AA, you must be an alcoholic although anyone can attend open meetings.

You can look for and join such a group around you. They are in many countries of the world. However, you can also pursue a personal path to recovery by following the underlying principle.

Here is a summary of the 12 Steps 3 from an AA member's perspective:

- We admitted we were powerless over alcohol—that our lives had become unmanageable.

---

[3] www.recovery.org

- We came to believe that a power greater than ourselves could bring us back to sanity.

- We made a decision to turn our will and our lives over to the care of God as we understood Him.

- We made a searching and courageous moral inventory of ourselves.

- We admitted to God, to ourselves, and to another human being the precise nature of our wrongs.

- We were completely ready to have God take away all these defects of character.

- We humbly asked him to take away our inadequacies.

- We made a list of all individuals we had harmed, and became ready to make amends to them all.

- We made direct amends to such persons wherever possible, except when to do so would harm them or others

- We continued to take personal inventory and quickly admitted it when we were wrong.
- We sought through prayer and meditation to enhance our conscious contact with God, as we understood him, praying only for awareness of his will for us and the power to carry that out.

Having had a spiritual wakening due to these steps, we tried to carry this message to other alcoholics, and to conform to these principles in all our affairs.

You can read further materials on the AA and its traditions. The important thing is to understand the underlying spiritual principle of the group. The principle comprises helping people to establish or restore a spiritual connection with God or some other higher power.

There are other similar "faith-based" methods by particular religious orientations. Meditation, prayer, and counseling with spiritual guides are useful and effective practices linked with this model. The addictive tendency can be removed by a combination of these activities.

While AA is about alcohol, the principle behind the organization can also be used to tackle other forms of addictions, whether substance or behavioral (sex, gambling, etc.).

There are questions for your individual contemplation from the spiritual model. The answers you give yourself to these questions will put you on a path to recovery. They will show you where you are and how you need to progress. Ruminating on them will provide you with insights of what to do to break free from addiction.

The questions include:

- What is the assessment of my life in light of my connection with God or a higher power?
- In light of my own critical beliefs and values, what is my life's evaluation result?
- Am I living in harmony with what I consider essential?

- Do I dedicate enough time to deliberating on my beliefs and values?
- Moral model of addiction and recovery implications

The basic idea of this model is this: "I'm responsible for creating the problem, and I'm responsible for solving it." It recognises proper motivation as the solution to the problem—addiction.

The healthy recovery application of the moral model include declaring to oneself that one started the addiction and is now deciding to put an end to it. For instance: "I decided to start using drugs, and now I'm choosing to stop."

As far as this model is concerned, a moral failure—a failure to do the right thing—leads to addiction. Recovery, therefore, comprises strengthening one's motivation or will to behave in a decent manner. It is the moral model that is more pronounced in traditional recovery methods. It is also from this perspective that the system of criminal justice approaches addiction.

Punishments for crimes related to addiction—such as drinking under influence, are envisioned to inspire people to act better. Making efforts to persuade a person to behave better is likewise a method associated with this model.

There is a less-known evidence-based treatment of addiction aligned with this model; it is known as Moral Reconation Therapy.

Conation is an old psychological jargon referring to human's ability to consciously and deliberately make decisions. The therapy aims to up the moral plane of decision-making.

There are questions for individual contemplation from the moral model. Answers to these questions will begin to give you insights on obtaining proper and potent motivation that will help you.

These questions include:

- Are there instances when I should exert more willpower and effort to remain on track?

- Can I deploy willpower to choose and behave better?

- Are there instances when I have to expend more effort to accomplish those things I know will assist me in recovering from addiction?

For example, you might be able to ascertain from these questions that exercising every day improves your mood and makes you feel better. You are then able to plan to do exercises more accordingly. Using the moral model, you are able to identify how you can hone your willpower to be able to do things that lessens your cravings and make resisting them easier.

Medical Model Of Addiction And Recovery Implications

The basic idea of this model is "I'm neither responsible for creating the problem nor responsible for solving it." It recognizes the solution to an addiction problem as consulting experts for guidance and treatments. Addicts that subscribe to this model acknowledge that they are ill and need help.

The healthy recovery application of this model comprises following the suggestions and advice of experts who are trying to help put an end to the addiction. After all, a typical patient in this case thinks like this: "I didn't plan on having these issues, and I'm short of ideas on how to get rid of them".

If your substance use or indulgence in an activity is out of control or bringing about problems, it's time to seek help. The sooner you try to get help, the better your chances of ful recovery.

Speak with your primary doctor or see a mental health expert, such as a doctor who specializes in addiction psychiatry or addiction medicine, or a licensed drug and alcohol counselor. These specialists will help put you on a path to recovery.

Book an appointment with a doctor if:

- You can't stop taking part in an activity or using a substance—drug, alcohol, inhalants, prescription drugs, etc.
- You continue using the substance or taking part in the activity regardless of the damage it causes.
- Your engagement in an activity or substance use has resulted in unsafe behaviour, such as unprotected sex, sharing needles and random acts of violence.
- You think you may be experiencing withdrawal symptoms after stopping the use of the substance or forsaking the activity.

If you're not prepared to approach a doctor, hotlines or help lines may be a good place to learn about treatment. There are many organizations—governmental and otherwise—out there who are interested in helping you find a solution to your addiction problem. You can find these lines listed on the internet.

If you identify the symptoms of any form of addiction in yourself or a person in your care, speak to your doctor about obtaining help. Your doctor can provide referrals to psychologists, addiction clinics, and other therapists; they can give therapy or prescriptions to treat a primary issue if you have one, such as social anxiety disorder or depression.

Compensatory Model Of Addiction And Recovery Implications

People who operate by this model have the notion that "I'm not responsible for creating the problem, but I am responsible for solving it".

As far as they are concerned, the solution to their addiction problem can be found in knowledge and skills. Folks who operate this model might try to seek to end their addiction on their own without acknowledging they have limitations.

The healthy recovery application of the compensatory model is in the addict trying to figure out a solution to their problem by combing through materials and applying what they learn.

It involves seeking help when you feel you need it, while trying to break free based on what you know and trying to use new habits to counteract addictions.

A typical person trying to recover via this model will say something like this: "I sure wish I didn't have these problems. But, since I do, I'm going to work out a way to solve them. I'll obtain some assistance if I need it."

People who choose this model are the kind that would read a material like this book, and try to work their way out of their addictions.

It is a model best suited to you if you have an internal locus of control. This is because you are able to take charge and tackle your addiction head on, while armed with insightful information.

There is an important point to note here, however. While you can decide to start a recovery from addiction on your own, you will most likely need help along the way. It is only wise to seek for help anytime you require it.

Fighting addiction is not an easy task; one is less likely to succeed when doing it without any form of support.

Recovery Is Possible

Generally and sincerely speaking, it is not enough to "just say no□. Instead, you can shield and heal yourself from all types of addiction by saying □yes□ to a number of other things.

To achieve this, you need to cultivate interest in things that give meaning to your life. To starve your addiction, take part in other activities—positive, value-adding non-addictive activities. This could include taking up other hobbies such as traveling, exercising, reading. Or going out with non-addict friends and participate in useful and healthy activities. It is a gradual process that takes time, but full recovery is possible.

To achieve total recovery, understand that your problems, especially those that may lead you into addiction, are usually transient. You also have to, perhaps most essentially, acknowledge that life is not always supposed to be gratifying. The human life is punctuated by ups and downs, highs and lows. Trying to disrupt that by getting hooked on dopamine is only going to worsen issues and engender a greater degree of less pleasurable consequences.

Staging An Intervention

Individuals struggling with addiction habitually deny that their use of substance or an activity is problematic and are unwilling to seek treatment. This is where an intervention could be helpful. An intervention affords a loved one a structured opportunity to make alterations before things get even worse, and can inspire a person to seek or accept assistance.

A lot of people find it difficult to seek and accepting assistance. But with the intervention of people who care about them, it becomes easier.

An intervention must be prudently planned and may be staged by friends and family in consultation with a doctor or specialist, such as an authorized drugs and alcohol counselor, or led by an intervention expert. It can include friends and family, and at times co-workers, an ordained priest or others concerned about the individual struggling with addiction.

These people assemble during the intervention to have a direct, candid discussion with the individual about the imports of addiction and appeal to him or her to seek and accept treatment. It's all about trying to help the addict get better by making a conscious effort.

When the addict experiences the intervention, they are able to do the needful, and the memory of it alone can keep them away from their addiction.

Preventing A Relapse

The moment you've been addicted to a substance or an activity, you're constantly at a danger of falling back into an addiction pattern. If you do begin to use the substance or take part in the activity again, it's possible you'll lose control over its use one more time — even if you've undergone treatment and you haven't used the substance or engage in the activity for a while.

Keep To Your Treatment Design

Keep track of your yearnings. It might appear that you're fully recovered and don't have to continue taking steps to stay clean. But your chances of remaining substance-free or avoiding going back to the activity will be much higher if you keep on seeing your counselor or therapist, attending support group gatherings and taking recommended prescription. So, whatever your stage of recovery, don't deviate from the plan, stick to it.

Avoid High-Risk Settings

Don't return to the vicinity where you used to smoke, drink alcohol or obtain your drugs. Stay away from your old drinking buddies, sexual partners, drugs crowd, etc.

Stay away from anything that can bring back a memory of the addiction. This significantly minimizes your chances of a relapse

Seek Help Immediately If You Relapse

If you start doing the activity or using the substance again, speak to your doctor, your counsellor, your mental health expert or any other person who can help you at once.

Substance Addiction: Integrated Treatment

In reality, substance addiction is a complex condition, and quitting typically takes more than a strong will or good intentions. Addictive substances modify the brain in ways that make it difficult to quit, even for those who desire to.

Luckily, researchers now have more knowledge than ever about how addictive substances affect the brain. They have also discovered treatments that can facilitate people's recovery from substance addiction and help them lead meaningful lives.

Integrated treatment is an all-inclusive programming that provides all of the therapeutic resources required to facilitate the healing of the individual spiritually, mentally, and physically.

There is no singular cause of addiction, although living with a mental health condition may raise the chances of developing a substance addiction—and vice versa. Every person is different.

In certain instances, a mental health disorder come before the development of a substance abuse. In other instances, mental health sign and symptoms are not obvious until after addiction has assumed control. Every now and then, these disorders are aggravated by substance use.

Addiction Has No Cure, Yet Addicts Can And Do Recover

Despite the fact that there is no remedy for any mental health condition, substance and behavioral addiction inclusive, a lot of people go on to lead amazing lives filled with optimism and courage.

Several research-based treatment interventions and therapies have been verified to be effective in remedying those who are living with any form of addiction. The important thing is receiving tailored treatment that is exhaustive and integrated.

When spiritual and therapeutic interventions, as well as enduring support are applied, individuals struggling with addiction do recover. Spiritual, physical, and mental wellness is cardinal to recovery.

Treatment for substance addiction by and large is not a cure, as is the case with most other prolonged ailments, such as heart disease, asthma, or diabetes.

Nevertheless, addiction is curable and can be effectively managed. Individuals who are on the road to recovery from an addiction will be at danger of a relapse for many years and probably for the rest of their lives.

Studies show that merging behavioral therapy with addiction treatment medications guarantees the greatest chance of success for a majority of patients. Treatment methods personalized to each patient's substance/activity use patterns and any co-occurring mental, medical, and social issues can result in sustained recovery.

The greater good news is the fact that substance addiction can be prevented. Prevention programs encompassing the media, schools, families, and communities are effective for precluding or decreasing substance use and addiction. Even though cultural factors and personal events influence substance use trends, young individuals tend to reduce their substance use when they consider it detrimental.

Thus, education and outreach are essential in assisting people in understanding the possible dangers of substance use. Parents, teachers and health care givers have critical roles in enlightening young individuals and preventing the use and addiction of any substance.

If you are free of any addiction, remain that way; stay away from anything that could lead to it. If you have any addiction, examine yourself, the addiction and your locus of control. Then decide how you intend to combine the different recovery models of addiction.

Choose the ones that best suit the peculiarity of your personality and addiction. Seek help if you believe you need any. Consult professionals to obtain a treatment or therapy plan. Then stick to the plan as if your life depends on it, because it does.

It might take time, but if you stick to your treatment plan, you will eventually get the better of your addiction. Religiously avoid situations and settings that can result in a relapse.

Chapter 5: 77 Biblical References That Show Alcohol Is Not For Christians

(Proverbs 20:1)

"Wine is a mocker, strong drink is raging: and whosoever is deceived thereby is not wise."

(Ephesians 5:18)

"And be not drunk with wine, wherein is excess; but be filled with the Spirit."

(Numbers 6:3)

"He shall separate himself from wine and strong drink, and shall drink no vinegar of wine, or vinegar of strong drink, neither shall he drink any liquor of grapes, nor eat moist grapes, or dried."

(Hosea 4:11)

"Whoredom and wine and new wine take away the heart."

(Leviticus 10:9)

"Do not drink wine nor strong drink, thou, nor thy sons with thee, when ye go into the tabernacle of the congregation, lest ye die: it shall be a statute forever throughout your generations."

(Isaiah 5:22)

"Woe unto them that are mighty to drink wine, and men of strength to mingle strong drink."

(Isaiah 5:11)

"Woe unto them that rise up early in the morning, that they may follow strong drink; that continue until night, till wine inflame them!"

(Isaiah 28:7)

"But they also have erred through wine, and through strong drink are out of the way; the priest and the prophet have erred through strong drink, they are swallowed up of wine, they are out of the way through strong drink; they err in vision, they stumble in judgment."

(Galatians 5:21)

"Envying, murders, drunkenness, reveling, and such like: of the which I tell you before, as I have also told you in time past, that they which do such things shall not inherit the kingdom of God."

(Proverbs 23:29-30)

"Who hath woe? Who hath sorrow? Who hath contentions? Who hath babbling? Who hath wounds without cause? Who hath redness of eyes? They that tarry long at the wine; they that go to seek mixed wine."

(Proverbs 23:31-32)

"Look not thou upon the wine when it is red, when it giveth his color in the cup, when it moveth itself aright. At the last it biteth like a serpent, and stingeth like an adder."

(Luke 1:15)

"For he shall be great in the sight of the Lord, and shall drink neither wine nor strong drink; and he shall be filled with the Holy Ghost, even from his mother's womb."

(Joel 1:5)

"Awake, ye drunkards, and weep; and howl, all ye drinkers of wine, because of the new wine; for it is cut off from your mouth."

(Genesis 9:21)

"And he drank of the wine, and was drunk; and he was uncovered within his tent."

(Judges 13:4)

"Now therefore beware, I pray thee, and drink neither wine nor strong drink, and eat not any unclean thing."

(Genesis 19:33)

"And they made their father drink wine that night: and the firstborn went in, and lay with her father; and he perceived not when she lay down, nor when she arose."

(Genesis 19:35)

"And they made their father drink wine that night also: and the younger arose, and lay with him; and he perceived not when she lay down, nor when she arose."

(Proverbs 31:4-5)

"It is not for kings, O Lemuel, it is not for kings to drink wine; nor for princes' strong drink: Lest they drink, and forget the law, and pervert the judgment of any of the afflicted."

(Habakkuk 2:15)

"Woe unto him that giveth his neighbor drink, that puttest thy bottle to him, and makest him drunken also, that thou mayest look on their nakedness!"

(Romans 13:13)

"Let us walk honestly, as in the day; not in rioting and drunkenness, not in chambering and wantonness, not in strife and envying."

(Titus 1:7)

"For a bishop must be blameless, as the steward of God; not self-willed, not soon angry, not given to wine, no striker, not given to filthy lucre."

(Proverbs 23:20-21)

"Be not among winebibbers; among riotous eaters of flesh: For the drunkard and the glutton shall come to poverty: and drowsiness shall clothe a man with rags."

(Isaiah 28:1)

"Woe to the crown of pride, to the drunkards of Ephraim, whose glorious beauty is a fading flower, which are on the head of the fat valleys of them that are overcome with wine!"

(Proverbs 21:17)

"He that loveth pleasure shall be a poor man: he that loveth wine and oil shall not be rich."

(Titus 2:3)

"The aged women likewise, that they be in behavior as becometh holiness, not false

accusers, not given to much wine, teachers of good things."

(1 Corinthians 6:10)

"Nor thieves, nor covetous, nor drunkards, nor revilers, nor extortioners, shall inherit the kingdom of God."

(Ecclesiastes 10:17)

"Blessed art thou, O land, when thy king is the son of nobles, and thy princes eat in due season, for strength, and not for drunkenness!"

(Luke 21:34)

"And take heed to yourselves, lest at any time your hearts be overcharged with surfeiting, and drunkenness, and cares of this life, and so that day come upon you unawares."

(Isaiah 19:14)

"The LORD hath mingled a perverse spirit in the midst thereof: and they have caused Egypt to err in every work thereof, as a drunken man staggereth in his vomit."

(Ezekiel 44:21)

"Neither shall any priest drink wine, when they enter into the inner court."

(1 Timothy 3:8)

"Likewise must the deacons be grave, not double-tongued, not given to much wine, not greedy of filthy lucre."

(1 Corinthians 5:11)

"But now I have written unto you not to keep company, if any man that is called a brother be a fornicator, or covetous, or an idolater, or a railer, or a drunkard, or an extortioner; with such a one no not to eat."

(1 Kings 16:9-10)

"And his servant Zimri, captain of half his chariots, conspired against him, as he was in Tirzah, drinking himself drunk in the house of Arza steward of his house in Tirzah. And Zimri went in and smote him, and killed him, in the twenty and seventh year of Asa king of Judah, and reigned in his stead."

(Isaiah 28:3)

"The crown of pride, the drunkards of Ephraim, shall be trodden under feet."

(Jeremiah 51:7)

"Babylon hath been a golden cup in the LORD's hand that made all the earth drunken: the nations have drunken of her wine; therefore the nations are mad."

(Romans 14:21)

"It is good neither to eat flesh, nor to drink wine, nor any thing whereby thy

brother stumbleth, or is offended, or is made weak."

(1 Corinthians 10:31)

"Whether therefore ye eat, or drink, or whatsoever ye do, do all to the glory of God."

(Deuteronomy 21:20-21)

"And they shall say unto the elders of his city, this our son is stubborn and rebellious, he will not obey our voice; he is a glutton, and a drunkard. And all the men of his city shall stone him with stones, that he die: so shalt thou put evil away from among you; and all Israel shall hear, and fear."

(Daniel 1:8)

"But Daniel purposed in his heart that he would not defile himself with the portion of the king's meat, or with the wine which he drank: therefore he requested of the

prince of the eunuchs that he might not defile himself."

(Romans 13:14)

"But put ye on the Lord Jesus Christ, and make not provision for the flesh, to fulfill the lusts thereof."

(1 Corinthians 6:12)

"All things are lawful unto me, but all things are not expedient: all things are lawful for me, but I will not be brought under the power of any."

(Romans 12:2)

"All things are lawful unto me, but all things are not expedient: all things are lawful for me, but I will not be brought under the power of any."

(1 Peter 4:3)

"For the time past of our life may suffice us to have wrought the will of the

Gentiles, when we walked in lasciviousness, lusts, excess of wine, reveling, banqueting's, and abominable idolatries."

(Jeremiah 25:27)

"Therefore thou shalt say unto them, Thus saith the LORD of hosts, the God of Israel; Drink ye, and be drunken, and spew, and fall, and rise no more, because of the sword which I will send among you."

(1 Timothy 3:2-3)

"A bishop then must be blameless, the husband of one wife, vigilant, sober, of good behavior, given to hospitality, apt to teach; Not given to wine, no striker, not greedy of filthy lucre; but patient, not a brawler, not covetous."

(1 Thessalonians 5:6-7)

"Therefore let us not sleep, as do others; but let us watch and be sober. For they

that sleep in the night; and they that be drunk are drunken in the night."

(Proverbs 26:9)

"As a thorn goeth up into the hand of a drunkard, so is a parable in the mouths of fools."

(Isaiah 5:12)

"They have harps and lyres at their banquets, tambourines and flutes and wine, but they have no regard for the deeds of the Lord, no respect for the works of his hands." (NIV)

(Isaiah 28:8)

"For all tables are full of vomit and filthiness, so that there is no place clean."

(Daniel 5:4)

"They drank wine, and praised the gods of gold, and of silver, of brass, of iron, of wood, and of stone."

(Hosea 7:5)

> *"In the day of our king the princes have made him sick with bottles of wine; he stretched out his hand with scorners."*

(Isaiah 56:12)

> *"Come ye, say they, I will fetch wine, and we will fill ourselves with strong drink; and tomorrow shall be as this day, and much more abundant."*

(Colossians 3:5)

> *"Mortify therefore your members which are upon the earth; fornication, uncleanness, inordinate affection, evil concupiscence, and covetousness, which is idolatry."*

(Ephesians 5:3)

> *"But fornication, and all uncleanness, or covetousness, let it not be once named among you, as becometh saints."*

(Romans 7:8)

"But sin, taking occasion by the commandment, wrought in me all manner of concupiscence. For without the law sin was dead."

(2 Timothy 3:2-4)

"For men shall be lovers of their own selves, covetous, boasters, proud, blasphemers, disobedient to parents, unthankful, unholy, Without natural affection, trucebreakers, false accusers, incontinent, fierce, despisers of those that are good, Traitors, heady, high-minded, lovers of pleasures more than lovers of God."

(Habakkuk 2:5)

"Yea also, because he transgresseth by wine, he is a proud man, neither keepeth at home, who enlargeth his desire as hell, and is as death, and cannot be satisfied,

but gathereth unto him all nations, and heapeth unto him all people."

(2 Peter 2:14)

"Having eyes full of adultery, and that cannot cease from sin; beguiling unstable souls: an heart they have exercised with covetous practices; cursed children."

(Mark 7:21-23)

"For from within, out of the heart of men, proceed evil thoughts, adulteries, fornications, murders, Thefts, covetousness, wickedness, deceit, lasciviousness, an evil eye, blasphemy, pride, foolishness: All these evil things come from within, and defile the man."

(Psalms 10:3)

"For the wicked boasteth of his heart's desire, and blesseth the covetous, whom the LORD abhorreth."

(2 Peter 2:19)

"While they promise them liberty, they themselves are the servants of corruption: for of whom a man is overcome, of the same is he brought in bondage."

(John 8:34)

"Jesus answered them, Verily, verily, I say unto you, Whosoever committeth sin is the servant of sin."

(Philippians 3:18-19)

"For many walk, of whom I have told you often, and now tell you even weeping, that they are the enemies of the cross of Christ: Whose end is destruction, whose God is their belly, and whose glory is in their shame, who mind earthly things."

(Romans 6:19)

"I speak after the manner of men because of the infirmity of your flesh: for as ye

have yielded your members servants to uncleanness and to iniquity unto iniquity; even so now yield your members servants to righteousness unto holiness."

(2 Peter 1:6)

"And to knowledge temperance; and to temperance patience; and to patience godliness."

(Proverbs 25:16)

"Hast thou found honey? Eat as much as is sufficient for thee, lest thou be filled therewith, and vomit it."

(Proverbs 28:7)

"Whoso keepeth the law is a wise son: but he that is a companion of riotous men shameth his father."

(Nahum 1:10)

"For while they be folden together as thorns, and while they are drunken as

drunkards, they shall be devoured as stubble fully dry."

(Luke 12:45-46)

"But and if that servant say in his heart, My lord delayeth his coming; and shall begin to beat the menservants and maidens, and to eat and drink, and to be drunken; The lord of that servant will come in a day when he looketh not for him, and at an hour when he is not aware, and will cut him in sunder, and will appoint him his portion with the unbelievers."

(Romans 6:12)

"Let not sin therefore reign in your mortal body, that ye should obey it in the lusts thereof."

(Titus 2:2)

"That the aged men be sober, grave, temperate, sound in faith, in charity, in patience"

(1 Corinthians 9:27)

"But I keep under my body, and bring it into subjection: lest that by any means, when I have preached to others, I myself should be a castaway."

(1 Corinthians 6:12)

"All things are lawful unto me, but all things are not expedient: all things are lawful for me, but I will not be brought under the power of any."

(Matthew 24:48-51)

"But and if that evil servant shall say in his heart, My lord delayeth his coming; And shall begin to smite his fellow servants, and to eat and drink with the drunken; The lord of that servant shall come in a day when he looketh not for

him, and in an hour that he is not aware of, And shall cut him asunder, and appoint him his portion with the hypocrites: there shall be weeping and gnashing of teeth."

(1 Corinthians 9:24-25)

"Know ye not that they which run in a race run all, but one receiveth the prize? So run, that ye may obtain. And every man that striveth for the mastery is temperate in all things. Now they do it to obtain a corruptible crown; but we an incorruptible."

(Jeremiah 35:6)

"But they said, We will drink no wine: for Jonadab the son of Rechab our father commanded us, saying, Ye shall drink no wine, neither ye, nor your sons forever."

(Jeremiah 23:9)

"Mine heart within me is broken because of the prophets; all my bones shake; I am like a drunken man, and like a man whom wine hath overcome, because of the LORD, and because of the words of his holiness."

NOTES

_____

_____

_____

_____

_____

_____

_____

_____

_____

_____

_____

_____

_____

_____

Printed in Great Britain
by Amazon

29442426R00092